YOUR

FATHER'S

STORY

Dad, I want to know everything about you...

GIVE THIS BOOK TO YOUR FATHER
TO FILL OUT AND RETURN BACK TO YOU

Follow us on social media!

Tag us and use #piccadillyinc in your posts
for a chance to win monthly prizes!

© 2019 Piccadilly (USA) Inc.

This edition published by Piccadilly (USA) Inc.

Piccadilly (USA) Inc.
12702 Via Cortina, Suite 203
Del Mar, CA 92014
USA

10 9 8 7 6 5 4 3 2 1

Printed in China

ISBN-13: 978-1-62009-151-7

YOUR

FATHER'S

STORY

$\mathcal{A}$s I entered this big world in the tiniest of forms, your fatherly embrace was there to greet and comfort me with love. You have been my security blanket, Guardian Angel, protector, teacher and disciplinarian. You're also my best source of encouragement, cheerleader and counselor. Pops you're everything to me and I want to know everything about you.

I know how to push your buttons and I think I know how to make you laugh. I know what every facial expression means and even figured out where your secret hiding place was, but I want to know more. I want to know how you became the person you are today. I want to know you when you were younger like me. Tell me stories from your childhood, tell me about Grandma and Grandpa but mostly tell me more about you.

I don't want to let time pass by without getting to know everything there is to know about you. I want to know more about myself through your eyes. I want to spend some time walking in your shoes, if only to see the world from your view. Please take the time to answer each question. No matter how small or insignificant you think it may be, this means everything to me. I want to know it all, the good, bad and in between. Your history will be written in these pages and while it's no substitute for the real you, I can look back and cherish each answer you wrote just for me.

Now your story begins...

CHAPTERS

CHAPTER I

About Our Family

"A HAPPY FAMILY IS
BUT AN EARLIER HEAVEN."

-George Bernard Shaw

$\mathcal{W}$hat was the name of your mother and father? Where and when were they born?

_____

_____

_____

_____

_____

_____

_____

_____

_____

_____

_____

_____

_____

_____

_____

_____

_____

_____

_____

_____

_____

_____

"WE NEVER KNOW
THE LOVE OF A PARENT TILL
WE BECOME PARENTS OURSELVES."

-Henry Ward Beecher

Describe your mom, my grandmother. Did she have any funny habits?

$\mathcal{D}$escribe your dad, my grandfather. Did he have any funny habits?

$\mathcal{D}$id you have any brothers or sisters, and did you want any? How did that change through time?

*W*ho was your favorite family member that wasn't your mom or dad and why were they your favorite?

_____

_____

_____

_____

_____

_____

_____

_____

_____

_____

_____

*W*hat was your favorite thing to do with your dad, my grandpa?

_____

_____

_____

_____

_____

_____

_____

_____

_____

_____

_____

*W*hat's the best advice you got from your mom and dad?

"DO NOT COMPLAIN BENEATH THE STARS ABOUT THE
LACK OF BRIGHT SPOTS IN YOUR LIFE."

-Bjørnstjerne Bjørnson

*W*hat is one thing I don't know about our family you think I should know now?

$\mathcal{W}$hat traditions do you hope to pass down to me and why?

"TRADITION IS NOT
THE WORSHIP OF ASHES,
BUT THE PRESERVATION OF FIRE."

-Gustav Mahler

Is there anything special about our family lineage? Do you know the origin of our family's name on both sides?

_____

_____

_____

_____

_____

_____

_____

_____

_____

_____

_____

_____

_____

_____

_____

_____

_____

_____

_____

_____

_____

_____

**"THE ONE THING
I WANT TO LEAVE MY CHILDREN
IS AN HONORABLE NAME."**

-Theodore Roosevelt

In our family, who do you have the most in common with and who did you have the biggest connection with?

Do we have any famous people, inventors or influencers in our family tree?

$\mathcal{D}$oes our family have any special recipes that have been passed down?

"EVERY MAN IS A QUOTATION
FROM ALL HIS ANCESTORS."

-Gustav Mahler

Do we have any special family antiques or heirlooms that have significant importance?

"OUR MOST TREASURED
FAMILY HEIRLOOMS ARE
OUR SWEET FAMILY MEMORIES."

- Unknown

How did your parents, my grandparents meet? How did their parents, my great grandparents meet?

*H*ow did you meet my mother? Describe your first encounter and your first date.

Did you ever experience love at first sight? Who was it with and how did you feel? What happened with this person?

_____

_____

_____

_____

_____

_____

_____

_____

_____

_____

_____

_____

_____

_____

_____

_____

_____

_____

_____

_____

_____

_____

_____

_____

_____

_____

_____

"WHO EVER LOVED
THAT LOVED NOT AT FIRST SIGHT?"

- William Shakespeare

$\mathcal{D}$id we lose any family members in a war?

$\mathcal{W}$hat are some of the most interesting facts about our family?

$\mathcal{W}$hat was your all-time favorite holiday of us together as a family and why? Before you became a dad, what was your most memorable holiday and why?

_____

_____

_____

_____

_____

_____

_____

_____

_____

_____

_____

_____

_____

_____

_____

_____

_____

_____

_____

_____

_____

_____

_____

_____

_____

"BLESSED IS THE SEASON
WHICH ENGAGES THE WHOLE WORLD
IN A CONSPIRACY OF LOVE."

-Hamilton Wright Mabie

CHAPTER II

When You Were Young

"A YOUTH IS TO BE
REGARDED WITH RESPECT.
HOW DO WE KNOW THAT HIS FUTURE WILL
NOT BE EQUAL TO OUR PRESENT?"

-Confucius

Where were you born? What is the first (earliest) memory you have from your childhood?

_____

_____

_____

_____

_____

_____

_____

_____

_____

_____

_____

_____

_____

_____

_____

_____

_____

_____

_____

_____

_____

_____

_____

"THE TWO MOST IMPORTANT
DAYS IN YOUR LIFE
ARE THE DAY YOU ARE BORN
AND THE DAY YOU FIND OUT WHY."

-Unknown

*D*id you have a favorite thing or toy as a child and why did you love it so much?

*D*id you have a nickname as a child? If so, how did you get it and how did you feel about it?

What do you remember about your childhood home?

"A MAN TRAVELS THE WORLD OVER
IN SEARCH OF WHAT HE NEEDS AND
RETURNS HOME TO FIND IT."

-George Moore

What was your favorite TV show, song and movie?

_____

_____

_____

_____

_____

_____

_____

_____

_____

_____

_____

_____

_____

_____

_____

_____

_____

_____

_____

_____

_____

_____

_____

_____

_____

_____

_____

"LET YOURSELF BE SILENTLY DRAWN
BY THE STRONGER PULL OF
WHAT YOU REALLY LOVE."

-Rumi

Did anyone ever tease you about anything when you were young and what was it?

$\mathcal{W}$hat did you want to be when you were little? In other words what did you dream about becoming when you grew up?

$\mathcal{W}$hat was the naughtiest thing you did as a child?

$\mathcal{W}$hat was your imagination like? Did you ever play pretend and what did you pretend to be?

What did you want most as a child that your mom and dad never gave you?

"IN TRUTH, PEOPLE CAN GENERALLY MAKE TIME
FOR WHAT THEY CHOOSE TO DO;
IT IS NOT REALLY THE TIME BUT
THE WILL THAT IS WANTING."

-John Lubbock

*W*hat were you afraid of when you were little (the dark, monsters under the bed, etc.) and how did your mom and dad comfort you?

What do you miss from your childhood?

_____

_____

_____

_____

_____

_____

_____

_____

_____

_____

_____

_____

_____

_____

_____

_____

_____

_____

_____

_____

_____

_____

_____

_____

_____

"WHAT WAS WONDERFUL ABOUT CHILDHOOD
IS THAT ANYTHING IN IT WAS A WONDER.
IT WAS NOT MERELY A WORLD FULL OF MIRACLES;
IT WAS A MIRACULOUS WORLD."

-G.K. Chesterton

$\mathcal{W}$ere you spoiled in any way? If so, by whom and how were you spoiled?

*W*here was your secret hiding spot as a kid?

_____

_____

_____

_____

_____

_____

_____

_____

_____

_____

_____

_____

*W*here was your favorite place to play and who did you usually play with?

_____

_____

_____

_____

_____

_____

_____

_____

_____

_____

_____

_____

Did you have a favorite family vacation, road trip or outing that you remember fondly from childhood?

What rules or chores did your parents give you that you swore you'd never give your own children (including me)?

_____

_____

_____

_____

_____

_____

_____

_____

_____

_____

_____

_____

_____

_____

_____

_____

_____

_____

_____

_____

_____

_____

_____

"IT IS A GOOD IDEA TO OBEY ALL THE RULES
WHEN YOU'RE YOUNG
JUST SO YOU'LL HAVE THE STRENGTH
TO BREAK THEM WHEN YOU'RE OLD."

-Mark Twain

$\mathcal{W}$hat was the town/city like that you grew up in? What was there to do there?

"THE STREETS LOOKED SMALL, OF COURSE.
THE STREETS THAT WE HAVE ONLY SEEN AS
CHILDREN ALWAYS DO I BELIEVE
WHEN WE GO BACK TO THEM."

-Charles Dickens

*W*hat childhood experiences did you have, that you wish I would have gotten to experience?

$\mathcal{W}$hat was your favorite food as a child and do you still like it?

$\mathcal{D}$id you ever dress up for Halloween, pull any pranks or did anyone ever scare you? What ghost stories and urban legends haunted your community?

"LISTEN TO THEM, THE CHILDREN OF THE NIGHT.
WHAT MUSIC THEY MAKE!"

-Bram Stoker

What were your hobbies when you were young? What did you enjoy?

_____

_____

_____

_____

_____

_____

_____

_____

_____

_____

_____

_____

_____

_____

_____

_____

_____

_____

_____

_____

_____

_____

_____

_____

"WHAT YOU FEED
IN YOURSELF THAT GROWS."

-Johann Wolfgang von Goethe

$\mathcal{W}$hat was the scariest moment from your childhood?

*W*hat's the biggest difference between your childhood and mine?

$\mathcal{W}$hat was the best moment from your childhood?

_____

_____

_____

_____

_____

_____

_____

_____

_____

_____

_____

_____

_____

_____

_____

_____

_____

_____

_____

_____

_____

_____

_____

_____

_____

"HOW STRANGE IT IS THAT WHEN I WAS A CHILD
I TRIED TO BE LIKE A GROWNUP,
YET AS SOON AS I CEASED TO BE A CHILD
I OFTEN LONGED TO BE LIKE ONE."

-Leo Tolstoy

CHAPTER III

Your Adolescent Years

"COMMON SENSE IS THE COLLECTION
OF PREJUDICES ACQUIRED
BY AGE EIGHTEEN."

-Albert Einstein

What did you hate/love the most about growing up?

$\mathcal{W}$hat was the hardest lesson for you to learn as you grew up?

"EVERY FAILURE IS A LESSON
LEARNED ABOUT YOUR STRATEGY."

-Thomas A. Edison

Who was your first crush and what happened with them?

_____

_____

_____

_____

_____

_____

_____

_____

_____

_____

_____

_____

_____

_____

_____

_____

_____

_____

_____

_____

_____

"SHE BLUSHED AND SO DID HE.
SHE GREETED HIM IN A FALTERING VOICE,
AND HE SPOKE TO HER
WITHOUT KNOWING WHAT HE WAS SAYING."

- Voltaire

$\mathcal{W}$ho was your first kiss? Where was it and what was it like?

Did you have a high school sweetheart? Spill the beans...

*W*hat/who influenced your style and taste as a teenager?

"ON MATTERS OF STYLE,
SWIM WITH THE CURRENT,
ON MATTERS OF PRINCIPLE,
STAND LIKE A ROCK."

-*Thomas Jefferson*

$\mathcal{D}$id you have a/any best friends? If so, who were they and why did you like them so much?

_____

_____

_____

_____

_____

_____

_____

_____

_____

$\mathcal{W}$ho was your celebrity crush and where did you first see them?

_____

_____

_____

_____

_____

_____

_____

_____

_____

_____

_____

$\mathcal{D}$id you have any favorite classes or subjects? Do you remember a particular teacher?

"I AM INDEBTED
TO MY FATHER FOR LIVING,
BUT TO MY TEACHER
FOR LIVING WELL."

-Alexander the Great

_D_id you ever get into trouble at school? What did you do and what was the punishment?

_____

_____

_____

_____

_____

_____

_____

_____

_____

_____

_____

_____

_____

_____

_____

_____

_____

_____

_____

_____

_____

_____

_____

_____

**"EVEN A FISH
WOULDN'T GET INTO TROUBLE
IF IT KEPT ITS MOUTH SHUT."**

-Korean Proverb

*W*hat was your favorite fad from your generation? What fad was the most embarrassing when you look back?

_____

_____

_____

_____

_____

_____

_____

_____

_____

_____

_____

*D*id you ever skip school? If you did, why?

_____

_____

_____

_____

_____

_____

_____

_____

_____

_____

_____

*W*hat's your most memorable school event (dance, game, etc.) and what made it so memorable?

$\mathcal{W}$hat kind of student were you and did you belong to any groups or cliques?

What does your yearbook say about you?

$\mathcal{W}$hat was your greatest school accomplishment?

$\mathcal{W}$ho was the biggest influence on your life growing up and was it positive or negative?

$\mathcal{D}$id you ever have any friends your parents didn't like?

"A FRIENDSHIP THAT CAN END
NEVER REALLY BEGAN."

-*Publilius Syrus*

$\mathcal{D}$id your dad, my grandpa ever do anything funny to a date when you began dating?

$\mathcal{W}$hat was the hardest thing you ever had to tell your parents as a teenager?

$\mathcal{W}$hat was the biggest lie you ever told growing up and who did you tell it to? Did anything ever happen?

$\mathcal{D}$id you ever experiment with anything? What was it and what happened?

$\mathcal{W}$hat is your biggest regret of your teenage years?

"NO SPACE OF REGRET
CAN MAKE AMENDS FOR ONE LIFE'S
OPPORTUNITY MISUSED."

-Charles Dickens

$\mathcal{W}$here did you hang out as a teenager and what did you do?

Did you ever think about college and where did you want to go? Why did you want to go there, and did you get to go? Why or why not?

When you got older, how did what you want to be change from when you were younger? What is the dream you wanted most for your life?

_____

_____

_____

_____

_____

_____

_____

_____

_____

_____

_____

_____

_____

_____

_____

_____

_____

_____

_____

_____

_____

_____

_____

"DREAMS ARE THE TOUCHSTONES
OF OUR CHARACTERS."

-Henry David Thoreau

What was the first car you wanted and why?

How did growing up in your decade differ from mine and what's the biggest difference?

Did you ever rebel? If so, what did you do?

$\mathcal{D}$id you have an afterschool job, or did you want one? Tell me more about it...

"YOUR WORK IS TO DISCOVER YOUR WORK
AND THEN WITH ALL YOUR HEART
TO GIVE YOURSELF TO IT."

-Unknown

$\mathcal{D}$id any world events or politics affect you growing up? How did you cope?

"IN POLITICS,
STUPIDITY IS NOT A HANDICAP."

-*Napoléon Bonaparte*

$\mathcal{W}$hat was your favorite summer vacation? How did you usually spend summers?

What was your most embarrassing moment in high school and how did you survive it?

"IF QUICK, I SURVIVE.
IF NOT QUICK, I AM LOST.
THIS IS DEATH."

-Sun Tzu

What wild and crazy ideas did you have for after high school that you never pursued?

Did you play sports, instruments or participate in school activities? What did you like and what were you good at?

*I*f you were going to pack a time capsule in high school for your future child to open, what do you think you would have packed for me to see and why?

Did you graduate high school? If so, how was it and what was the highlight of graduating?

$\mathcal{D}$id you dream about getting married and what kind of wedding you'd have? Who did you think you'd marry and what kind of wedding did you want?

_____
_____
_____
_____
_____
_____
_____
_____
_____
_____
_____
_____
_____
_____
_____
_____
_____
_____
_____
_____
_____
_____
_____

"TO GET THE FULL VALUE OF JOY
YOU MUST HAVE SOMEONE TO
DIVIDE IT WITH."

-Mark Twain

What's the most important thing you learned in school that actually helped you in the real world?

What other hopes and dreams did you have for your life?

CHAPTER IV

Things You Learned About Life

"IT IS BETTER TO LIVE YOUR OWN
DESTINY IMPERFECTLY THAN TO LIVE
AN IMITATION OF SOMEBODY ELSE'S
LIFE WITH PERFECTION."

-Anonymous, The Bhagavad Gita

*W*here did your life take an unexpected turn and how did it happen?

"LIFE BELONGS TO THE LIVING,
AND HE WHO LIVES
MUST BE PREPARED FOR CHANGES."

-Johann Wolfgang von Goethe

$\mathcal{W}$hat's the most important thing you learned about relationships?

_____
_____
_____
_____
_____
_____
_____
_____
_____
_____
_____
_____
_____

$\mathcal{I}$s there a secret or key to happiness?

_____
_____
_____
_____
_____
_____
_____
_____
_____
_____
_____
_____
_____

What was the hardest period of your life and why?

Was having a family as rewarding as you thought it would be?

_____

_____

_____

_____

_____

_____

_____

_____

_____

_____

_____

_____

_____

_____

_____

_____

_____

_____

_____

_____

_____

_____

_____

_____

"AFTER A GOOD DINNER
ONE CAN FORGIVE ANYBODY,
EVEN ONE'S OWN RELATIONS."

-Oscar Wilde

What life challenges were the most difficult for you?

"THE GEM CANNOT BE POLISHED
WITHOUT FRICTION,
NOR MAN PERFECTED
WITHOUT TRIALS."

-Confucius

$\mathcal{W}$as there any area of your life you neglected that you wish you hadn't?

*W*hat life event brought you the most emotional pain?

What mistake did you make that you'd never want your children to repeat?

"BE PATIENT,
EVEN IF EVERY POSSIBILITY
SEEMS CLOSED."

-Rumi

$\mathcal{D}$id you ever experience peer pressure? What happened and how did you handle it?

_____

_____

_____

_____

_____

_____

_____

_____

_____

_____

_____

$\mathcal{W}$hat do you think is the root of all evil and why?

_____

_____

_____

_____

_____

_____

_____

_____

_____

_____

_____

_____

$\mathcal{W}$hat did you learn about becoming a dad and parent?

"THE SOUL IS HEALED
BY BEING WITH CHILDREN."

-Fyodor Dostoevsky

What was the scariest thing about raising a child?

$\mathcal{W}$hat did you learn about true friendships?

_____

_____

_____

_____

_____

_____

_____

_____

_____

_____

_____

_____

_____

_____

_____

_____

_____

_____

_____

_____

_____

_____

_____

_____

"WE ARE LIKE ISLANDS IN THE SEA,
SEPARATE ON THE SURFACE
BUT CONNECTED IN THE DEEP."

- William James

$\mathcal{D}$id you learn anything interesting about yourself on your life's journey, what was it?

_____

_____

_____

_____

_____

_____

_____

_____

_____

_____

_____

_____

_____

_____

_____

_____

_____

_____

_____

_____

_____

_____

"A GOOD TRAVELER
HAS NO FIXED PLANS AND IS NOT
INTENT ON ARRIVING."

-Lao Tzu

$\mathcal{W}$hat is the most important lesson you've learned about people?

$\mathcal{D}$o you think life's fair? Tell me the way it is or isn't...

What golden rule do you want me to live by?

*H*ow did you know when you were in love?

"NOBODY IS PERFECT UNTIL
YOU FALL IN LOVE WITH THEM."

-Unknown

What is life's most precious commodity that shouldn't be wasted?

What should I do if I can't forgive someone?

$\mathcal{W}$hat moments in your life do you relish the most?

_____

_____

_____

_____

_____

_____

_____

_____

_____

_____

_____

_____

_____

_____

_____

_____

_____

_____

_____

_____

_____

_____

_____

_____

_____

"THERE IS NO MOMENT OF DELIGHT
IN ANY PILGRIMAGE
LIKE THE BEGINNING OF IT."

-Charles Dudley Warner

$\mathcal{D}$id you ever feel like giving up? What did you do? What should I do if I ever feel like giving up on something?

$\mathcal{W}$hat is most valuable to you in this life?

Tell me about a crossroads in your life and what you did. How did you make a decision about what to do?

_____

_____

_____

_____

_____

_____

_____

_____

_____

_____

_____

_____

_____

_____

_____

_____

_____

_____

_____

_____

_____

_____

_____

_____

_____

_____

"IT DOES NOT MATTER HOW
SLOWLY YOU GO AS LONG AS
YOU DO NOT STOP."

-Confucius

How does the idea of becoming a grandparent make you feel?

Did you ever want to travel the world? If you could go anywhere you wanted, where would you go and why?

$\mathcal{H}$ow did you handle betrayal in your life?

What rule did your parents teach you that turned out to be the most important rule of all?

_____

_____

_____

_____

_____

_____

_____

_____

_____

_____

_____

_____

_____

_____

_____

_____

_____

_____

_____

_____

_____

_____

_____

_____

"WHEN I LET GO OF WHAT I AM,
I BECOME WHAT I MIGHT BE."

-Lao Tzu

$\mathcal{H}$as anything from your past haunted you? What was it?

*I*n what ways do you feel blessed?

$\mathcal{D}$id you ever experience a miracle, if so what?

"THERE ARE TWO WAYS TO LIVE:
YOU CAN LIVE AS IF NOTHING IS A MIRACLE;
YOU CAN LIVE AS IF EVERYTHING IS A MIRACLE."

-Albert Einstein

$\mathcal{W}$hat are you most thankful for in your life today?

_____

_____

_____

_____

_____

_____

_____

_____

_____

_____

_____

_____

_____

_____

_____

_____

_____

_____

_____

_____

_____

_____

_____

"LET US BE GRATEFUL TO THE
PEOPLE WHO MAKE US HAPPY;
THEY ARE THE CHARMING GARDENERS
WHO MAKE OUR SOULS BLOSSOM."

-Marcel Proust

Tell me what you know about the phrase "nothing lasts forever" and "don't know what you've got until it's gone."

$\mathcal{D}$ad, is honesty always the best policy?

"HALF THE TRUTH IS OFTEN
A WHOLE LIE."

-Benjamin Franklin

*W*hat bad trait do you have that always got you into trouble? Do I have it too?

_____

_____

_____

_____

_____

_____

_____

_____

_____

_____

_____

*W*hat should I never waste energy on?

_____

_____

_____

_____

_____

_____

_____

_____

_____

_____

_____

_____

_____

*W*hat's one of the hardest things we will have to do in life?

*W*hat have you learned about trusting people?

What's your biggest regret in life?

_____

_____

_____

_____

_____

_____

_____

_____

_____

_____

_____

_____

_____

_____

_____

_____

_____

_____

_____

_____

_____

_____

_____

_____

_____

_____

"REMORSE IS
THE POISON OF LIFE."

-Charlotte Brontë

CHAPTER V

Growing Older

"I LIVE IN THAT SOLITUDE
WHICH IS PAINFUL IN YOUTH,
BUT DELICIOUS IN THE
YEARS OF MATURITY."

-Albert Einstein

What do you wish someone had told you about life when you were younger?

"WE ARE WHAT WE REPEATEDLY DO.
EXCELLENCE, THEN,
IS NOT AN ACT, BUT A HABIT."

-Aristotle

Does life get easier as you grow older?

Looking back, what do you wish you'd made more time for?

What is your proudest life accomplishment thus far?

"TO ACCOMPLISH GREAT THINGS,
WE MUST DREAM AS WELL AS ACT."

-Anatole France

*W*hat is your favorite memory about fatherhood in general?

"THE HEART OF A FATHER
IS THE MASTERPIECE OF NATURE."

-Antoine François Prévost

What are you currently looking forward to in your life right now?

How much sacrifice did you have to make in life? In what ways and was the reward worth the sacrifice?

$\mathcal{D}$id you ever think you'd end up where you are now in life?

_____

_____

_____

_____

_____

_____

_____

_____

_____

_____

_____

_____

_____

_____

_____

_____

_____

_____

_____

_____

_____

_____

_____

_____

_____

_____

"TWENTY YEARS FROM NOW
YOU WILL BE MORE DISAPPOINTED
BY THE THINGS YOU DIDN'T DO
THAN BY THE ONES YOU DID DO."

-*Mark Twain*

If you could have met anyone famous at any point in your life, who would it have been and why?

"WE ALL CARRY THE SEEDS
OF GREATNESS WITHIN US,
BUT WE NEED AN IMAGE
AS A POINT OF FOCUS IN ORDER
THAT THEY MAY SPROUT."

-Epictetus

$\mathcal{W}$here did you always want to live that you never got the chance?

$\mathcal{W}$hat should I never forget to do?

Who or what was your best teacher about life?

_____

_____

_____

_____

_____

_____

_____

_____

_____

_____

_____

_____

_____

_____

_____

_____

_____

_____

_____

_____

_____

_____

_____

_____

_____

_____

_____

_____

"A TRUE TEACHER IS ONE WHO,
KEEPING THE PAST ALIVE,
IS ALSO ABLE TO UNDERSTAND
THE PRESENT."

-Confucius

What is one thing that didn't turn out the way you'd hoped and how did you wish it had turned out?

*W*hat problems of the world today trouble you?

"OF ALL YOUR TROUBLES,
GREAT AND SMALL,
THE GREATEST ARE THE ONES
THAT DON'T HAPPEN AT ALL."

-Thomas Carlyle

Did you ever experience unrequited love?

**"'TIS BETTER TO HAVE
LOVED AND LOST
THAN NEVER TO HAVE LOVED AT ALL."**

-Alfred Lord Tennyson

Does wisdom come from age?

$\mathcal{W}$hat was the one thing you always tried to shelter your child/children from?

What are your plans for retirement?

"TIME SPENT IN LAUGHTER
WHEN ONE IS RETIRED
IS WELL INVESTED."

- Unknown

$\mathcal{I}$n what ways are you still like a child?

_____

_____

_____

_____

_____

_____

_____

_____

_____

_____

_____

_____

_____

_____

_____

_____

_____

_____

_____

_____

_____

_____

_____

"EVERY CHILD IS AN ARTIST.
THE PROBLEM IS HOW TO REMAIN AN ARTIST
ONCE HE GROWS UP."

-Pablo Picasso

$\mathcal{W}$hat can you never be too careful about?

$\mathcal{W}$hat lessons did you learn about money that you want me to know?

_____

_____

_____

_____

_____

_____

_____

_____

_____

_____

_____

$\mathcal{W}$hat makes you laugh now, that made you furious back then?

_____

_____

_____

_____

_____

_____

_____

_____

_____

_____

_____

_____

What is the one thing you want people (family, friends, etc.) to remember most about you?

_____

_____

_____

_____

_____

_____

_____

_____

_____

_____

_____

_____

_____

_____

_____

_____

_____

_____

_____

_____

_____

_____

"LIFE SHRINKS OR EXPANDS
IN PROPORTION
TO ONE'S COURAGE."

-Anaïs Nin

$\mathcal{W}$hat can I expect out of life as I grow older?

_____

_____

_____

_____

_____

_____

_____

_____

_____

_____

_____

_____

_____

_____

_____

_____

_____

_____

_____

_____

_____

_____

_____

_____

_____

_____

_____

"TOO MANY OF US ARE NOT LIVING OUR DREAMS
BECAUSE WE ARE LIVING OUR FEARS."

-_Les Brown_

In what way did you wish your life had turned out different?

CHAPTER VI

Becoming a Dad

"A TRULY RICH MAN IS ONE
WHOSE CHILDREN RUN INTO HIS ARMS
WHEN HIS HANDS ARE EMPTY."

-Anonymous

POST PHOTO
HERE

*J*ake your favorite picture of me and post it here. Tell me why you love it so much.

$\mathcal{W}$hat is one thing you wish we'd done together, that we haven't had a chance to yet?

"THE LURE OF THE DISTANT AND
THE DIFFICULT IS DECEPTIVE.
THE GREAT OPPORTUNITY
IS WHERE YOU ARE."

–John Burroughs

*W*hat was the scariest thing about fatherhood?

Did you always know you wanted to become a dad?

_____

_____

_____

_____

_____

_____

_____

_____

_____

_____

How did you feel the first time you found out my mom was pregnant?

_____

_____

_____

_____

_____

_____

_____

_____

_____

_____

_____

$\mathcal{W}$hat was one of our most special moments as father and child?

_____

_____

_____

_____

_____

_____

_____

_____

_____

_____

_____

_____

_____

_____

_____

_____

_____

_____

_____

_____

_____

_____

_____

_____

_____

_____

"BECOMING A FATHER IS EASY ENOUGH,
BUT BEING ONE CAN BE VERY ROUGH."

-Wilhelm Busch

If you had to do fatherhood all over again, would you change anything? If so, what?

"BLESSED INDEED IS THE MAN
WHO HEARS MANY GENTLE VOICES
CALL HIM FATHER."

-Lydia Maria Francis Child

*G*ive me your best advice about becoming a new parent.

What do you and I have most in common (features, traits, etc.) and how soon did you notice it?

Describe the bond you and I share.

$\mathcal{T}$ell me your secret thoughts about me as a kid in my most mischievous phase.

_____

_____

_____

_____

_____

_____

_____

_____

_____

_____

_____

_____

_____

_____

_____

_____

_____

_____

_____

_____

_____

_____

_____

_____

_____

_____

_____

_____

_____

"WHEN CHILDREN
ARE DOING NOTHING,
THEY ARE DOING MISCHIEF."

-Henry Fielding

*W*hen or what time were you the proudest of me?

When you think of me, what's the first thing that comes to mind?

$\mathcal{W}$hen I was a child, what were your hopes and dreams for my life?

*L*ooking back, what were our craziest and funniest moments together?

_____
_____
_____
_____
_____
_____
_____
_____
_____
_____
_____

*B*e honest, what did I do that drove you crazy?

_____
_____
_____
_____
_____
_____
_____
_____
_____
_____
_____
_____

*A*s I was growing up, what career path did you think I'd pursue?

"DREAM BIG
AND DARE TO FAIL."
-Norman Vaughan

$\mathcal{W}$hat do you hope I learned from and what would you never want me to repeat?

$\mathcal{H}$ow good of a job do you think you did as a dad?

_____

_____

_____

_____

_____

_____

_____

_____

_____

_____

_____

_____

_____

_____

_____

_____

_____

_____

_____

_____

_____

_____

_____

_____

"NOBLE FATHERS
HAVE NOBLE CHILDREN."

-Euripedes

I could be the biggest brat when...

"I'M ALWAYS DOING THINGS I CAN'T DO.
THAT'S HOW I GET TO DO THEM."

-Pablo Picasso

$\mathcal{W}$hat was the one thing I gave or give you, others can't?

How did you pick my name? Did you almost name me something else and what other names did you consider?

What was the one thing you wish you knew before becoming a father?

"IT IS NOT WHAT YOU DO FOR YOUR CHILDREN,
BUT WHAT YOU HAVE TAUGHT THEM
TO DO FOR THEMSELVES,
THAT WILL MAKE THEM SUCCESSFUL HUMAN BEINGS."

-Ann Landers

*T*ell me about myself as an infant. What funny story should I know that happened when I was really young?

_____

_____

_____

_____

_____

_____

_____

_____

_____

_____

_____

_____

_____

_____

_____

_____

_____

_____

_____

_____

_____

_____

"IT IS A HAPPY TALENT
TO KNOW HOW TO PLAY."

-*Ralph Waldo Emerson*

Describe my terrible twos.

$\mathcal{W}$hen I have kids, what karma do you hope comes back to me. What hellishness did I put you through?

$\mathcal{W}$hat do you think is my best personality trait and who did I get it from?

_____

_____

_____

_____

_____

_____

_____

_____

_____

_____

_____

_____

_____

_____

_____

_____

_____

_____

_____

_____

_____

_____

_____

_____

_____

_____

_____

"PERSONALITY IS ONLY RIPE
WHEN A MAN HAS MADE THE TRUTH HIS OWN."

-Søren Kierkegaard

$\mathcal{W}$hat birthday of mine stands out as most special, why?

"LET US NEVER KNOW WHAT OLD AGE IS.
LET US KNOW THE HAPPINESS TIME BRINGS,
NOT COUNT THE YEARS."

–Ausonius

*W*hat is your most treasured memory of just you and I?

Looking back on all the bad things I did as a child, which one secretly made you laugh?

$\mathcal{H}$ow did you feel the first time you saw me after I was born?

_____

_____

_____

_____

_____

_____

_____

_____

_____

_____

_____

_____

_____

_____

_____

_____

_____

_____

_____

_____

_____

_____

_____

_____

_____

_____

_____

"MY MOTHER GROANED,
MY FATHER WEPT,
INTO THE DANGEROUS WORLD I LEAPT."

- William Blake

How are we the most different?

Tell me about one of my most embarrassing moments in school and how we got through it together?

What was the hardest talk you ever had to have with me?

Did you pass down any advice or techniques that your dad, my grandfather gave you?

_____

_____

_____

_____

_____

_____

_____

_____

_____

_____

_____

_____

_____

_____

_____

_____

_____

_____

_____

_____

_____

_____

"KEEP YOUR FACE
ALWAYS TOWARD THE SUNSHINE—
AND SHADOWS WILL FALL BEHIND YOU."

- Walt Whitman

*W*hat punishment was the hardest to give me and why?

Describe our relationship in your own words.

*W*hat things did you have to learn as you went along? Who did you regularly call for advice on being a father?

_____

_____

_____

_____

_____

_____

_____

_____

_____

_____

_____

_____

_____

_____

_____

_____

_____

_____

_____

_____

"THE MORE I READ,
THE MORE I ACQUIRE,
THE MORE CERTAIN I AM
THAT I KNOW NOTHING."

- Voltaire

$\mathcal{W}$hat was the greatest invention for dads, in your opinion?

$\mathcal{W}$hat was the one thing you worried about the most where I was concerned?

What moments as a father made you laugh the most?

What life lesson do you feel is most important for me to learn?

"THE BEST AND MOST BEAUTIFUL THINGS
IN THE WORLD CANNOT BE SEEN OR EVEN TOUCHED;
THEY MUST BE FELT WITH THE HEART."

-Helen Keller

$\mathcal{W}$ho or what was your biggest helper as a dad?

_____

_____

_____

_____

_____

_____

_____

_____

_____

_____

_____

_____

_____

_____

_____

_____

_____

_____

_____

_____

_____

_____

"YOU HAVE NOT LIVED TODAY
UNTIL YOU HAVE DONE SOMETHING
FOR SOMEONE WHO CAN
NEVER REPAY YOU."

-John Bunyan

*W*hat have you always tried to protect me from?

_____

_____

_____

_____

_____

_____

_____

_____

_____

_____

_____

_____

*A*s a father what did you want more of, that you never had enough of?

_____

_____

_____

_____

_____

_____

_____

_____

_____

_____

_____

_____

In what ways was fatherhood not all it was cracked up to be?

Did having a child/children stand in the way of your dreams?

"LIMITATIONS LIVE ONLY IN OUR MINDS.
BUT IF WE USE OUR IMAGINATIONS,
OUR POSSIBILITIES BECOME LIMITLESS."

-Jamie Paolinetti

*W*ere you afraid of becoming like your father?

_____

_____

_____

_____

_____

_____

_____

_____

_____

_____

_____

_____

_____

_____

_____

_____

_____

_____

_____

_____

_____

"ONE FATHER IS MORE THAN
A HUNDRED SCHOOLMASTERS. "

-George Herbert

*W*hat have you always wanted to ask me but never did?

*W*hat do you think is the most important role/task of a father?

Looking for more?

Similar titles available by Piccadilly:

300 Writing Prompts

300 MORE Writing Prompts

500 Writing Prompts

3000 Questions About Me

3000 Would You Rather Questions

Choose Your Own Journal

Complete the Story

Your Grandfather's Story

Your Mother's Story

The Story of My Life

Write the Story

300 Drawing Prompts

500 Drawing Prompts

Calligraphy Made Easy

Comic Sketchbook

Sketching Made Easy

100 Life Challenges

Awesome Social Media Quizzes

Find the Cat

Find 2 Cats

Time Capsule Letters

WWW.PICCADILLYINC.COM